Kreider + O'Leary are a poet and a  to make work in sites such as pris locations, landscape gardens and Dr Kristen Kreider is Reader in Poe Holloway, University of London. James O'Leary is Lecturer in Architecture at The Bartlett School of Architecture, University College London.

Falling is typeset in Arnhem, designed by Fred Smeijers.

Writtle University College Library

3 3012 00076 8913

Whittle University College
Library

FALLING
Kreider + O'Leary

COPY PRESS

The Copy Press Limited
51 South Street
Ventnor
Isle of Wight
PO38 1NG

copypress.co.uk

Commune no. 8
Editor: Yve Lomax
Reader: Vit Hopley
Copy-editor: Sara Peacock
Design: Ivor Williams

Front cover © Kreider + O'Leary

Printed on Munken Print White
no.18 80gsm. Munken Print White
standard products are FSCTM
and PEFC certified.
Printed and bound in England.

First edition © Copy Press Ltd/
Kreider + O'Leary, 2015

Kreider + O'Leary assert the moral
right to be identified as the authors
of this work.

A catalogue record for this book is
available from the British Library

ISBN-13 978-1-909570-01-6

All rights reserved. No part of this
publication may be reproduced, stored
in a retrieval system, or transmitted in
any form or by any means, electronic,
mechanical, photocopying, recording
or otherwise, without the prior
permission of the publishers.

This book is sold subject to the
condition that it shall not, by way of
trade or otherwise, be lent, re-sold,
hired out or otherwise circulated
without the publisher's prior consent
in any form of binding or cover other
than that in which it is published and
without a similar condition including
this condition being imposed on the
subsequent purchaser.

TABLE OF CONTENTS

MAN ON MOON

Imagine a ground, untouched. Imagine further a stone, unturned in the untouched ground. Imagine its stillness and sediment. Imagine the silence. Imagine all of this, out here, beyond horizon; that is, beyond our knowable ground. Now imagine a movement – hurtling towards it! A trajectory locked in steel! This is our message from the Dreamworld, and it will have impact. This is beyond all doubt. But before that, a tender scene:

Three men, each wearing a suit, are sitting in the close confines of a spacecraft. These men are going to the moon! When they get there, they will land their spacecraft and get ready to take a walk.

Houston —
I'd just like to evaluate the, uh, the various paces that a person can use to travel on the lunar surface ...

One of these men, touching down upon the moon's surface, will get over-excited and start bounding around all over the place. He will keep bounding around with higher and longer steps – and this will seem like a really fun thing to do.

Houston —
You do have to be, alright, you do have to be, uh, a bit careful to keep track of where your center of mass is ...

He is, after all, the very first man to set foot on the moon.

Houston —
Sometimes it takes about two or three paces to, uh, make sure that you got your feet underneath ya ...

But there is a risk that he will lose his centre of gravity.

F	Houston —
A	About two to three – or maybe four easy paces ...
L	
L	So he is reprimanded by Ground Control, who tell him to stop.
I	
N	Houston —
G	... can bring you into a fairly smooth, uh, *stop*.

When they depart, these men will leave behind a sign to indicate that this ground, once untouched, has been traversed; that space has been occupied. Some will believe this to be true. Others will become convinced that all of this is fake and, rather than having landed on the surface of the moon, these men were actually somewhere in a desert in Mexico. But whether they believe it or not, everyone will be watching. *Everyone* will be watching these men landing and this man bounding somewhere out of this world and live on TV.

Arguably, when Icarus flew too close to the sun, so close that it melted his wings, that was partly because the Greek sun was only thought to be a few thousand feet from the earth. The stars were not much further. However, careful examination of the two-dimensional motion of the stars and the planets eventually revealed a third dimension, and the sky opened up into space.

F
A
L
L
I
N
G

An apple falls

     THWACK!

A man, Sir Isaac Newton, understands that all objects in the universe are falling toward one another with the same force that pulls this apple invisibly toward the ground. This is the same force that, as Newton would surmise, links the tides to the lunar cycle, and keeps the planets moving on their elliptical paths around the sun, the moons around their planets, as was described, but not explained, by Johannes Kepler. This is the same force that, following the explosion of a phenomenally hot, extraordinarily dense primordial atom, caused the gases of hydrogen and helium to condense into clouds, out of which the stars were formed, then the galaxies, then more galaxies in clusters, and onwards and outwards and ever expanding made the universe. The same force that allows us to slip so easily into this world, then presents us with continual challenges once we are in it, especially when we endeavour to become upright and, later, to practise architecture.

The attractive force that Newton identified became the basis for a natural law, represented through a mathematical formula. This force also became a concept, represented by the word 'gravity'. As a mathematical formula describing a natural law, gravity could be applied perfectly to the world. However, as a word, gravity seemed like a magical entity: its referent an invisible, unseen force. How could a force make itself felt across seemingly empty space, without any medium or perceivable contact? As Newton concedes: 'Some persons will probably be ready to enquire what is the cause of this hidden virtue of gravity which is here attributed to the heavenly bodies. To this the only answer is, that this cause is as yet one of Nature's secrets: and perhaps it will ever remain so.' Having been ushered into a paradigm where nature operated according to cause and effect, as a cue ball scatters its coloured constellation across the billiard table, gravity remained an effect without a cause and this, inevitably, prompted criticism. The philosopher Leibniz labelled Newton's conception of gravity 'occult', while fellow scientist Christiaan Huygens deemed it 'absurd'. Newton, himself – the great physicist, alchemist and theologian – admitted that the idea of gravity acting on objects at a distance was 'so great an absurdity, that ... no man who has in philosophical matters a competent faculty of thinking [could] ever fall into it.'

So an object (apple) falls and a concept ('gravity') arises: the concept of a force that could be witnessed, but not known; an attractive force with a forceful effect on the thinking of the time. Indeed, the concept of gravity would affect a paradigmatic shift away from a universe in motion and into a world of falling. So this beginning, falling and rising toward the end of the seventeenth century would mark a conceptual turn.

Following this turn for a moment, we arrive at what appears to be a slight deviation: a question. A question that has dogged philosophy for centuries. What is the relationship between the word and the world? Deceptively simple in appearance, this question extends language beyond a mere act of naming, and far beyond the idea that language is simply a mimetic representation of reality. Implicit in this relationship between the word and the world is a performative act: one that organises what it enunciates.

In the seventeenth century, this relationship between word and world was understood analogically through its relation to analytical geometry. Just as analytical geometry (a symbolic system imbued with phenomenal reference) was used to measure the world, so language (another symbolic system, also imbued with phenomenal reference) was used to describe it. Now, up until this story started – that is, up until the apple

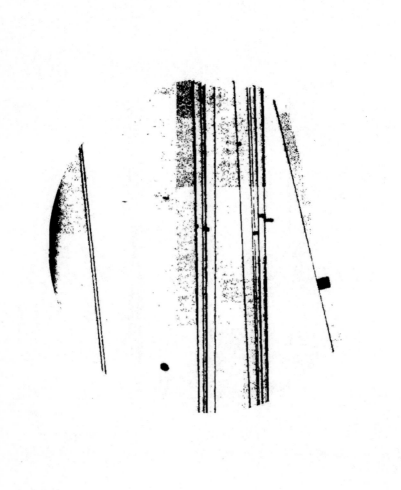

fell – the phenomenal world that analytical geometry had described so successfully was a world governed by the laws of motion. However, once Newton suggests that the motion of massive bodies separated in space could be explained by an attractive force actually pulling these bodies toward one another – in other words, once the world of simple motion turns into a world of falling – the most adequate means of describing the world becomes a mathematical formula: one *without* phenomenal reference. Somewhat paradoxically, as Cathy Caruth says, analytical geometry and language could no longer adequately describe the world.

As a result, and as a much later philosopher will argue, philosophy after Newton becomes a confrontation with questions of how to talk about falling. More precisely, the philosophical 'problem of reference', which this later philosopher Paul de Man will associate specifically with the post-Newtonian era, is actually a problem of how to refer to falling.

According to the pragmatist John Dewey, a problem does not exist without a solution. This is not to say that every problem finds its resolution – far from it. Rather, until one proposes a solution, there exists not a problem, but simply a situation. We can therefore assume that the question of the relationship between the word and the world does indeed present a problem for philosophy, for it is a philosopher who comes up with its solution: Immanuel Kant.

Writing in *Critique of Judgement*, Kant presents his solution to the problem of reference. Firstly, he distinguishes between 'metaphysics' and 'transcendental philosophy'. On the one hand, metaphysics is understood as an expansion of Newton's laws of motion: an empirically derived set of laws that are dependent on direct observation and knowledge of the world for their meaning. On the other hand, transcendental philosophy is construed as an entirely conceptual system: one that makes possible thinking about the empirical world in the first place. With his development of philosophy as a transcendental conceptual system, Kant thus solves the problem of reference – or, more precisely, the problem of how philosophy can refer to bodies in a world of falling – by freeing philosophical discourse from any need or obligation to know the world at all. Philosophy comes to know itself, instead, as precisely that which does not directly know or speak of worldly phenomenon.

This is, indeed, a neat solution, but one that bears a contradiction, a *resistance*, within its very design. Paul de Man locates this resistance to the transcendental project at two significant points in Kant's writing, both of which involve a body. The first instance is when Kant illustrates his distinction between metaphysics and transcendental philosophy through recourse to how each relates to the phenomenon of bodies in motion or, more specifically, how each addresses the question of what causes a change in bodies in motion. In this instance, metaphysical law would state that changes in a body in motion must have an *external* cause. This is because, in Newtonian terms, all non-linear motion is caused by an external force. In contrast, transcendental law would simply state that all changes in a body in motion must have *some* cause, thus leaving open the possibility that the change in bodies in motion is caused by something internal to the very system of thought through which these bodies are conceived. From this example, one can see how metaphysics addresses questions about the world through recourse to natural law, thereby showing its dependence upon empirical studies of the world. Transcendental philosophy, however, addresses questions about the world without recourse to natural law, thereby showing its independence from empirical study and, with

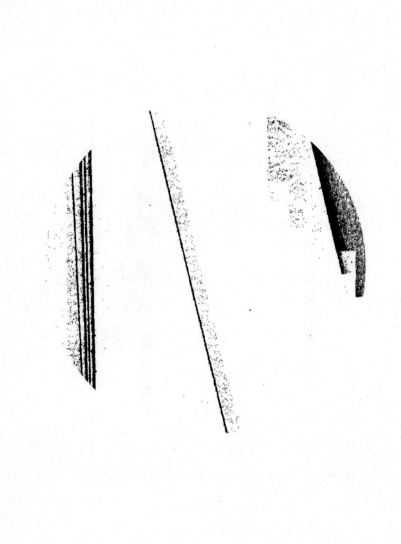

this, abandoning any need to refer to the physical world in addressing questions relating to it. As this example shows, metaphysical thought differs from transcendental thought through the relationship that each has to the physical world. Crucially, it is the very fact that Kant's example *shows* us this difference that suggests its inherent resistance to his transcendental project.

By introducing this example, Kant effectively sets up a secondary definition of transcendental philosophy: one that sits alongside his conceptual definition so that we might be able *see* and *grasp* his understanding. The example, offered up as an object of study, thus undermines the very premise of a purely conceptual project.

Another instance where a body appears in Kant's writing, further suggesting a resistance at the heart of his transcendental project, is when he invokes the *Glieder* – a whole, unified and upright body made up of a number of parts or members – as the figure for his philosophy. This figure stands in direct contradistinction to the falling, empirical body: the body to which philosophy could no longer refer, and for which it had therefore relinquished responsibility. Thus, transcendental philosophy relinquishes direct reference to the empirical body in its self-definition; yet, paradoxically, it is only by reintroducing it figuratively, embodying it within language, that it is able to do so.

In an interesting twist to this story, Paul de Man makes a direct comparison between the figure of the *Glieder* in Kant's philosophical writing and the figure of a puppet, or *Gliedermann*, in a short story by Heinrich von Kleist entitled *On the Marionette Theatre.* In this story, the principal dancer of a ballet company attends a marionette theatre and, during the course of the event, notes the 'perfection' of the puppet dance. As the dancer points out, this perfection is purely mechanical since the puppeteer is able to manipulate the puppet's centre of gravity by simply pulling on the strings. There is nothing of the clumsiness of the human being. Instead, the limbs are 'what they should be: dead, mere pendula, governed only by the law of gravity'. This puppet body is Kant's philosophical body. Through this further figuration, the philosophical body as a series of articulated parts not only moves, but dances; and not only dances, but does so gracefully. Still, any grace attributed to the marionettes in Kleist's story lies not in the puppets, themselves, but in the transformations that occur between the puppeteer and the puppet. That is to say, the puppet – and, by analogy, Kant's philosophical project – has no motion in and of itself, being composed of lifeless, mechanical limbs. Instead, all of its mobility lies in the text that spins between the puppeteer and the puppet. And it is through this text that the puppet, that philosophy, appears to be rising and falling as if no such thing as gravity existed, as if it had achieved a kind of grace.

So it was and it was not. A man with an apple falling on his head. Philosophy construed as a self-reflexive system where a figure is moving with beauty and grace; where the body – lifeless, mechanical and devoid of referential weight – falls only to ascend. An object propelled with such force that it escapes the earth's gravitational pull and begins its slow, steady descent to the moon.

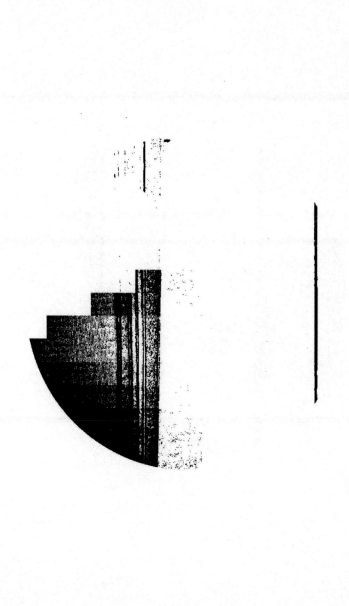

A man is standing on a busy street corner, holding up a sign and speaking through a loud hailer. The man, looking very intent, is explaining to no one how, in the end, everything will rise. And not just some things, he says, but everything. Everything will rise in the end, he is saying. Every single thing.

For a sign to become a sign, it must be repeated at least once. Which is why, when they saw the second tower going up, they knew that this was no ordinary building. No, this great column of steel and glass, doubled, would mark an architectural entry into the realm of the symbolic. There it would accrue value and meaning on a representational plane as much as it would on its site here in Lower Manhattan. Years would pass, films would be made and the structure, clearly recognisable as a formal element along the syntagm of the New York City skyline, would come to signify: Capitalism, Globalisation, American Imperialism along with various combinations and permutations of these associations. At the time of their completion on 4 April 1973, the buildings at 1 World Trade Center and 2 World Trade Centre were the tallest in the world. On 7 August 1974 a wire was stretched, illegally, between the rooftops of the two buildings and the figure of a wirewalker could be seen moving back and forth, along the wire, against the sky.

The man steps onto the wire and out of the world. He steps out of the governing of the world. He steps out of the governing and into the un-governing of the world. This is a conscious choice.

To move between the banality of this world and the extraordinary. To renounce. To enter exile. To become, in the words of Catherine Clément, a 'casualty of time'. Such movement and becoming are characteristic of what she calls 'syncope' and are experienced – indeed, chosen – by those she describes as 'syncope-people'. Writing a whirlwind across cultural forms and disciplinary contexts, she upturns this syncope or 'stop-time' in a vast array of examples from fainting, depression and the dead of night to the mystic's ecstasy, the philosopher's thought and the dance of the whirling dervish.

In these and further instances the rules typically governing the world are, for a moment, suspended such that the subject is both present and absent to herself. Typically eschewed by Western philosophies and cultural traditions, more readily embraced by those of the East, the experience of syncope interrupts the conventions of language and temporality through which we construct a coherent and sovereign sense of self. To choose syncope is thus to renounce the laws by which we are governed; more, the laws that we employ to govern ourselves. Herein lies its political potentiality. Mahatma Gandhi – his strategy of non-violence to oppose oppressive rule; his tactics of renunciation through which to achieve this – is amongst those considered syncope-people.

The man will remain on the wire for 45 minutes. During this time he will traverse the wire's 42-metre length, turn, traverse its length again, return. This will happen eight times in total. At one point he will kneel down and look at the street where a crowd will be gathered to watch. At another point he will lie on his back and look at the sky where clouds will accumulate and blow.

For the ancient Greeks, the word *meteora* encompassed all of the phenomena of the sky including the movements of the heavenly bodies as well as atmospheric conditions such as

clouds,

rain, hailstorms, tornados and the direction and force of the wind. The term could also denote certain earthly occurrences such as earthquakes and volcanos, considered to have similar causes as their celestial counterparts. Changeable and formless, the *meteora* are difficult to study, let alone control, and for this reason the philosopher Michel Serres will later claim that meteorology has become the repressed content of history,

be this the history of philosophy or science or both. The weather, affecting everything and everyone, is so unpredictable a force that it has been excluded from closed rational orders and strict scientific study. Science happens inside. The laboratory – indeed, any closed system – can ultimately be seen as providing protection against perceived turbulence. (So the puppets continue their dance with grace and ease ...)

The exclusion of the *meteora* from the history of Western philosophy and science finds its visual analogue in the early experiments of architect Filippo Brunelleschi. In his efforts to develop a system of representation capable of accurately depicting illusionistic space, Brunelleschi first depicted the baptistery of San Giovanni on the surface of a small panel using single-point perspective. He then cut a peephole into this panel at the vanishing point of the perspectival composition. Standing behind the panel and holding up a mirror to its front, a viewer could look at the depicted architectural scene reflected on the mirror where it appeared in perfect perspective. Remarkably, while Brunelleschi represented all of the buildings on the panel in single-point perspective, he made no attempt to depict the sky. Instead, he chose merely to show it by adding a reflective material to the surface of the panel that was capable of mirroring the 'real' sky. Pointing to this act of subterfuge, art history will later claim that the mirrored sky in Brunelleschi's experiment testifies to the limits of perspective since one cannot represent within this closed system the sky without measure, the wind blowing the clouds.

At each end of the wire two police officers will be waiting to take the man into custody. More police officers will be circling in a helicopter overhead. If he does not come down from the wire of his own accord they will be forced to pluck him from the thin air themselves. The ancient Greek word *herma* refers to a square or rectangular pillar of stone often found on the sides of roads, particularly at their crossings. The *herma* could also be found at the boundaries between lands where they would signal transition. From this word derives the name of the Greek god of boundaries: Hermes, the messenger god, with his winged feet and headgear. This word is also the root of the word 'hermeneutics'. Hermes, himself, was the forerunner of the angels, from *angelos*, the Greek word meaning message. These angels are the messengers of god and we see them moving between the earthly and divine realms throughout the history of Western art, religion and thought. In Ezekiel we see them with four wings and four faces: those of a man, a lion, an ox and an eagle. In the visions of Hildegard von Bingen they appear as an army of bright spirits arrayed concentrically in the shape of a crown. Some have forms like human forms and feet like human feet. Some wear helmets, carry torches and are surrounded by cloud. Some are simply eyes and wings, and in each eye there is a mirror and in each mirror there is a human form. Others just shine like red dawn. St Thomas of Aquinas invokes angels in his efforts to think through the mechanics of the universe to consider Aristotle's idea of intermediary movers. Other philosophers including Locke and Descartes use angels to contemplate non-experiential knowledge. Angels make their appearance as sculptural objects, painted figures, poetic images, stained glass in the guise of guardian angels, avenging angels,

falling angels,

cherubs. They are the dancer, the diver, the gymnast, the wind. One bears witness to historical ruin. Many consider them as immaterial entities, but in one old tradition they are half fire, half ice.

Another man will describe the sense of trepidation he felt just at the moment when the wirewalker stepped foot onto the wire. There clearly had not been enough time. It was, as he will later attest, the worst wire he had ever strung. The team of people involved had been up all night, most of it spent hunched in a small ball remaining as still as possible in order to escape the detection of the night guard. Then, when the guard had finally left and they got their chance to move into position, clamp one end of the wire onto one building, shoot the bow and arrow with the wire attached over to the second building, nearly miss it and find themselves clambering to the very edge of the rooftop to retrieve it, there was barely be enough time or, for him, enough energy to reel the weight of the wire metre by metre across the night sky and, eventually, clamp it securely onto the second building just before dawn when the morning watchman returned. He was anxious, on edge, stiff, cold and mentally and emotionally exhausted from the whole thing of the wirewalker with his crazy, single-minded idea. He, both accomplice and friend, falling for it; they, concocting this wild scheme to string this wire across the rooftops of the two tallest buildings in the world, and then working with a team of outcasts and dreamers to actually do it! The entire plot was utterly insane and they had worked at it ceaselessly for months. Now they had completed their task and it was, without a doubt, the worst wire he had ever strung. He felt chided by rationality and overwhelmed by the very scale of their ambition. When he looked at the wire he saw only a limp and lifeless string onto which the wirewalker was setting first one foot, then another, then a third step resisting the fall of his own body, carrying himself forward and settling his face into an expression that meant, they all knew, they could relax. The man would walk the wire and the two friends, estranged, would never work together, never really even speak to one another, again.

In 1852, Elisha Otis developed a safety device designed to prevent an elevator cab from falling if one of its supporting cables should break. The first Otis elevator was installed in

1857 in the E.W. Haughtwhat & Company building on 488 Broadway in Manhattan. Years later, the architect Rem Koolhaas would claim that this invention, coupled with the use of steel frames in building construction and with developments in central air conditioning, allowed for architecture's ascent into the sky; more specifically, that the construction of the Flatiron building in 1902, with its 22 floors extending over 300 feet into the sky and fed by no fewer than six elevators, marked the beginning of the age of

skyscrapers.

More buildings followed – the World Tower Building, the Beneson Building, the Equitable Building – each repeating their respective square footage of the Manhattan grid in a multiplication of 'virgin sites' stacked floor upon floor upon floor. Obviating any deference to the restrictions and vicissitudes of ground conditions, architecture yielded only to programme; that is, to the organisation of its interior into discreet zones. So its occupants shuttled up and down in vertical cabs, encountering each floor as a discrete entity: business sector, living quarters, shopping district, theatre cluster. This ideal of Skyscraper as a closed system – a city within a city, a work of total architecture providing for every need – acted as a kind of laboratory for the cosmopolite or what Rem Koolhaas would call the 'ultimate vehicle of emotional and intellectual adventure'. Eventually, and pushing the logic of Skyscraper to its limits, programme gave way to pure artifice. The ceiling of 228–32 West 42nd was decorated to represent a blue sky in which electric lights twinkled and an ingenious assembly of optical apparatus produced the effect of clouds sweeping by overhead.

Sergeant Charles Daniels of the New York City Port Authority will appear that evening on the CBS Evening News. He will

describe the moment that he and a fellow officer first observed the tightrope dancer, because you couldn't really call him a walker, approximately half way between the two towers. Sergeant Daniels will explain how, upon seeing the officers, the man began to smile and then to laugh, provoking them by moving close to one end of the wire before swiftly turning around just out of reach. Everybody was spellbound in the watching of it and Sergeant Daniels, observing that the man was not about to come down, because he seemed to be enjoying himself so much, then informed the wirewalker's friend that they would have to dislodge him by force. At this point, Sergeant Daniels will say to the camera, this other man began speaking to the wirewalker in French, being that he was a Frenchman, and telling him that he had to come down from the wire. Sergeant Daniels will then say that he believed personally he figured he was watching something nobody was ever going to see again in the world. It was once in a lifetime. It was the apex of excitement.

In 1954, a large urban housing project known as Pruitt–Igoe was first inhabited by residents of the most poverty-stricken district of St Louis, Missouri. The complex consisted of 33 eleven-storey buildings with a total of 2,870 apartments. The high-rise buildings were equipped with 'skip-stop' elevators that alighted only at the first, fourth, seventh and tenth floors, both to save costs and to lessen congestion. The overall plan, designed by architect Minoru Yamasaki, who later designed the World Trade Center towers in Lower Manhattan, was praised by *Architectural Forum* as 'vertical neighbourhoods for poor people'. By the late 1960s the complex had become internationally renowned for its endemic poverty, crime and racial segregation. By 1971 as many as 16 of the buildings were left boarded up and abandoned. The others remained in a state of decay or completely destroyed by vandalism. When asked about his project, Yamasaki was quoted as saying 'I never thought people were that destructive'. As the complex deteriorated, the entire project was seen as one of the largest-scale failures in the history of urban planning and, by the early 1970s, the 33 buildings of the Pruitt–Igoe complex were scheduled for demolition in a contained explosion. The first building went down at 3pm on 16 March 1972. The second building went down on 22 April 1972. More demolitions followed throughout the following three years, and the entire site was reduced to rubble by 1976.

On the street below a woman is looking up. She is waiting for the man to appear. She knows, or thinks that she knows, that the man will appear. She trusts that he will appear. This woman is the wirewalker's lover, and has been for some time. A shy woman, he approached her and charmed her with his wirewalker ways until, after a time, she fell for him and now here she is standing on a New York street corner looking up. She is looking up when, finally, he makes his appearance on the wire. He is there and she is here looking up and, soon, she is instructing those around her to look up also. Look! Look! She is telling those on the street. Look, a wirewalker! He's walking! The people on the street look up and, seeing a man on a wire, stop what they are doing to watch. They watch as the figure moves back and forth, so small against the sky between the buildings. They are, they know, so small also, but on the ground and in a crowd so it is different. The man on the wire takes their breath. His movements are more like dance, they think, and if the woman on the street had not been there they may simply have walked right past – some heading to work; some heading nowhere. They may never have stopped and so never have seen the man, the woman's lover, walking the wire, who would no longer be her lover when he came down. Later in her life, when asked about the event, the woman will describe it as extraordinary. So, so beautiful. *C'était comme s'il marchait sur un nuage.* It was like he was walking on a cloud, she will say, and this comment will be edited into a documentary film.

Walking is to the urban system what speaking is to language. So goes the analogy developed by Michel de Certeau who, standing at the top of the World Trade Center looking down, will enact a shift in perspective from this totalising view to the more localised actions of the

streetwalkers

below. This fall to street level is a plunge into everyday where spaces are made to exist and emerge through the hustle and jostle of a peripatetic flow. Feet fall and cars honk and dust rises and people pass and this is the taste of the city. This is the atmosphere only imagined when it was viewed as a skyline of verticals. Here is the beautiful mess we are in – this phenomenon, this crowd – and if prose is a movement from A to B, then poetry is the dance.

It is morning and the turning of the large wheel signals that someone is coming up in the elevator. Now is the time to perform. The man thinks about his death. They all think it. But he does not want to die – far from it. He wants to carry his life across the wire and, compelled, makes no effort at all to resist.

Water compels us. In our encounter with an unknown element, we move toward its protean strangeness. Water attracts us, just as it attracts the air that, in turn, is attracted to the ground. Water falls and we fall into it. Or perhaps we are thrown into it. Or perhaps it washes over us in a tidal wave that leaves us choking and breathless and fearful of a

death by drowning

whereby we, with water, become formless: a subject-less, porous membrane.

Elizabeth 'Lisa' Smith was born on 27 September 1959 and jumped from the Golden Gate Bridge on 11 April 2004. She is one of over 1,300 people who have jumped to their deaths from this Art Deco bridge since it was first suspended over the San Francisco Bay in 1937. The bridge spans 1.2 kilometres. The amount of wire used totals 128,750 kilometres. Most people die upon the trauma of impact, but some are still alive when they hit the water and are either overwhelmed by the strong current or die of hypothermia. Some survive the fall. Lisa's mother, brother and sister will reflect on her life. They will describe her as having been different from other people, something they really noticed when she was around 14 years old. Lisa was more angelic, her mother will say; she was not of this world. Having been diagnosed with paranoid schizophrenia in her teens, Lisa lived most of her life in a series of care homes and independent living centres. In the period leading up to her jump Lisa had been physically unwell. Her teeth were just so rotted, her mother will explain, and they thought it was because of the medication and also because she drank a lot of Coke. Lisa had to have all of her teeth removed and she walked around for one week with this cavernous opening, this void in her face, before making a decision to step off the bridge and out of the world. Lisa's jump was recorded, and the footage was edited into a documentary film that many would find distressing and some distasteful.

There is a line of thinking that runs throughout the history of natural philosophy in which everything, everywhere is continually falling – always. The world is composed of these particles that fall and these particles are falling forever. Sometimes they fall fast and sometimes they fall slow. Sometimes they fall straight and other times, as Lucretius suggests, they are inclined to swerve. However they fall, so this line of thinking goes, the entire universe – from the microcosmic to the macrocosmic – is composed of this falling material: individual particles all falling that, taken together, make up the world. We, ourselves, comprise such matter, our bodies and thoughts but a rain of stuff. Faster, we move with the wind and the fire. Slower, we are

roots and
rhizomes.

After a time the accumulating clouds become so dense, the wind blows with such force, and there is no longer any reason to remain, so the man on the wire comes down.

The Slapstick Body
was born in 1897, the same year as cinema.

The Slapstick Body
is a working man, and honest; the still, small, suffering centre
of hysteria.

The Slapstick Body
is the great stone face, the human mop, the figure of hyperbole
– no, he is hyperbole's vertigo.

Although first making his appearance on the vaudeville
stage, it was through the medium of film that this figure
really found form. Use of a camera meant that he could leave
the theatre behind – he could go almost anywhere. We, in turn,
but still confined, could watch him on screen in a train or a boat,
up a tree, under a table, in a house, in battle with the material
world. Camera angles, technical tricks, editing and projection
all became intrinsic to his particular rhythm. He thus owes his
appearance, which is to say his existence, to this particular mode
of mechanical reproduction.

The Slapstick Body
appears through the repetition of gesture and effect.

The Slapstick Body
disappears through the repetition of gesture and effect.

The notion of rhythm is intrinsic to human activity. Through
rhythm, we distinguish types of human behaviour, both
individual and collective. We also project this sense of rhythm
into things and events beyond the human sphere. The result
is a 'vast unification of man and nature under time' that,
as the linguist Émile Benveniste discovers, is the very condition

of the word *rhythm* itself.

The Slapstick Body
is perfectly integrated into the composition of the shot.

The Greek word for rhythm, ρυθμός, first appears in the writing of Ionian philosophers. More specifically, it appears in the work of Leucippus and Democritus, two of the creators of atomism. For these materialist philosophers, the universe comprises individual particles: atoms in continual motion, forever falling, that join together in order to act as bodies. These bodies become recognisable by their mutual differences in 'form', 'order' and 'position', and in this context the philosopher Democritus first uses the word ρυθμός to designate 'form' understood as the disposition or configuration of atoms. So, for example, water and air differ from one another in the *form*, ρυθμός, that their constituent atoms take.

The Slapstick Body
has perfect timing, that of synchronicity amidst sequence.

From this original usage, ρυθμός comes to designate the form of a belief, an institution, the human character, a state of balance. The phrase 'to give form to' suggests to picture or to localize. Form itself is said to be balanced, beautiful, proportioned, reproducible. Clearly, the meaning of ρυθμός shifts slightly with each of these different contexts and usages; however, one meaning remains constant throughout: the understanding of ρυθμός as form that is improvised, momentary and changeable. All of which is to say, that throughout these vacillations of the word's history, ρυθμός consistently – and somewhat paradoxically – designates form that is never fixed, but always subject to change, thus recalling its original designation for the form of all things in the natural world, as understood by the atomist philosophers.

The Slapstick Body
is a confrontation with force, such as a typhoon or a hurricane.

How, then, does ρυθμός come to be associated with the notion
of rhythm as we now understand it? It is when the afore-
mentioned consideration of the formal structure of things
meets a theory of measure as applied to the figures of dance.
This meeting occurs in Plato's discussion of musical intervals.
In the course of this discussion, Plato distinguishes between
two types of interval. Firstly, there are intervals characterised
spatially as being 'high' or 'low', and these are the combinations
of harmony. Secondly, there are numerically regulated intervals
characterised temporally as being 'fast' or 'slow', and these
relate to the movements of the body. Here Plato uses the word
ρυθμός to designate the latter: the measured movements of
the dancing body. So, in this context, the word ρυθμός retains
its original meaning as a form of movement. However, what
Plato adds is his specific appreciation of ρυθμός as the form
of movement made by the human body – more specifically, the
'arrangement of figures into which this movement is resolved'.
ρυθμός thus comes to designate corporal movement bound
by the law of numbers: a form – or, more specifically, a figure
– determined by measure and numerically regulated. At which
point we arrive at the modern understanding of rhythm.

The Slapstick Body
jerks and pulses.

The Slapstick Body
defies gravity.

The Slapstick Body
does not speak easily.

The Slapstick Body
topsy turvy.

All of this suggests that if rhythm is the 'vast unification of man and nature under time', it is less because man gleans his appreciation of rhythm from the ebb and flow of the natural world, and more because man imposes his own sense of regulated and measured time onto the movements of the world – and, indeed, other men. For to control the durations and repetitions of human activity is to control human behaviour. In this sense, if the notion of rhythm is intrinsic to human activity, then its regulation is intrinsic to government.

The Slapstick Body
is a product of industry, which he counters with perfect plasticity.

The Slapstick Body
accelerates along the regulated rhythm of progress.

During his lifetime, film-maker Frank Bunker Gilbreth (1868–1924) made over 250,000 feet of 35mm motion picture film recording human activity across a range of working environments including traditional trades, factories and administrative environments. These recordings were made using a camera model that, developed before 1910, required hand-cranking. Depending on light conditions and other factors of the shoot, sometimes the camera was cranked slow and other times it was cranked fast. The result is that sometimes there is a speed-up effect and other times a slow-motion effect in the footage. In an effort to counter this effect, obtaining accurate timings for each of his films, Gilbreth placed a specially calibrated clock called a microchronometer near the camera operator. This accuracy was required given that Gilbreth's objective was to develop a comprehensive visual

record of how workers completed certain tasks, with the aim of improving their working methods. Gilbreth's 'motion studies', as they became known, were eventually combined with the 'time studies' of Frederick Winslow Taylor. Taylor's studies were based less on an analysis of film footage and more on the direct observation of labour; however, they had a related aim of improving the standard time it takes to complete a given task.

The Slapstick Body
is the frenzy of the material world.

The refinement and eventual integration of time and motion studies in the early part of the twentieth century allowed for the analysis of labour processes, and particularly industrialised labour processes, in a scientific context. This, in turn, led to the development of a work-improvement system that was highly influential in the management of industrial labour. Standardising human activity for better work efficiency, Taylorism would allow for a significant increase in the speed of both manual and industrial production. It would also play a major role in Henry Ford's development of the assembly line, where the speed of production was increased even further by combining the division, distribution and repetition of the activity required to produce an object with the virtual immobilisation of the human body: a denial of skilled and variable gesture in favour of regulated, mechanistic motion.

The Slapstick Body
is the complex registration of an historical moment, its equal and opposite reaction.

The Great War, to end all wars, was fought between 1914 and 1918, a product of the age of industry and deploying machine weaponry for the first time throughout the battlefields and skies of Europe. The scale of atrocity of this war was immense.

F
A
L
L
I
N
G

Thousands upon thousands of men dwelling in scars across the landscape were confronted by violence at such a speed, and of such intensity, that it left them speechless, limbless, faceless. Bodies fell and were broken. Those that returned were beyond recognition, leading those who remained to question how it is we understood being human in the first place. Bipedalism? Laughter? Technology? Our ability to reason? Our capacity to imagine? Amidst the reality of this frightening scene they found comfort in the body on screen who they could see falling and rising, falling and rising again. This body felt no pain. This body did not break. This body refused to die. Caught in the grips of a Sisyphean logic, dead-pan and beyond all suffering, this body kept falling and rising, falling and rising again ...

The Slapstick Body
is the consequence of action.

The Slapstick Body
embodies violence without power.

The Slapstick Body
goes to war in a too-big coat and shoes that don't fit.

The slap stick is an object, much like a paddle, with two wooden slats that sound a loud and corporeal smack when struck together. Often used as a percussion instrument in orchestras and ensembles, the slap stick is capable of introducing a dramatic element into musical composition; for example, a clap of thunder, a violent repercussion, a sleigh ride. In the realm of performance, the slap stick allows actors to hit one another repeatedly, seemingly brutally, but with little force actually transferring from the object. In this respect the slap stick generates great effect with deviant cause – as an object, it is a sign of pure artifice.

The Slapstick Body,
who is never injured, breaks every bone in his body.

The Slapstick Body,
subjected to violence, is turned into a thing.

Pain is a completely subjective experience. Its existence is
signalled through noise and expression. Having no metric,
and beyond our capacity to narrate, its particularity is
communicated only through analogy or metaphor. Confronted
with the body in pain, we are solicited to use our imagination;
enjoined to project ourselves into another's situation, thereby
fostering cognition and feeling: all of this in order to cultivate
the understanding and compassion necessary for an empathic
exchange. But it takes time, of course, and distance for us
to respond in this way. Without this – for example, when
confronted with fast, repetitive and hyperbolic acts of violence
– we can only react. And our reaction is, quite simply, to laugh.
Ha ha ha ha ha.

The Slapstick Body
is wracked, jolted, shoved, cajoled, smacked, upended,
overturned.

The Slapstick Body
is man-handled, boot-kicked, clod-hopped, box-eared, thrown
across the room to crack the audience's ribs.

The Slapstick Body
is laughter and pain in a paradoxical twist.

The Slapstick Body
is the first instrument of violence against himself.

Advances in contemporary warfare have made combat less immediate. We can shoot our enemy from a great distance, bomb them from the air. War mediated by the machine means that our responsibility dwindles. We do not look our enemies in the eye. Death happens to those *over there.* Still, bullets and missiles are nothing without contiguity and impact: a 'direct shot' is the pride of the bourgeois marksman. He takes aim, squeezes the trigger and releases the ammunition, which must make contact with its intended recipient in order to register effect. Imagine, then, the surprise – the shock, even – when, on 22 April 1915, a battalion of French and Canadian troops in the northern Ypres Salient began to die, one after another, without any sign of gunfire or bombing, and no traces of blood. In the first attack of its kind, a specially formed German 'gas regiment' had managed to secretly install thousands of gas cylinders along the front line of battle. Then, at exactly 6pm, under the command of Colonel Max Peterson, they opened the 1,600 large and 4,130 small chlorine-filled cylinders to a prevailing north-northeast wind. The resulting cloud expanded to nearly six kilometres in width and 900 metres in depth, floating over the Allied trenches and filling the environment directly around the soldiers with a deadly fume. 'Fuzzying' the notion of the direct hit and introducing an ungovernable warfare, the toxic cloud executed each man in turn by turning that which seemed utterly safe and familiar against him: the very air he breathed. The German intellectual Peter Sloterdijk will point to the battle at Ypres as indicative of three defining characteristics of the twentieth century: the practice of terrorism, the concept of product design and environmental thinking.

The Slapstick Body
denies metaphysics.

The Slapstick Body
drinks too much.

The Slapstick Body
is a fleeting composite of action without expression.

The same gas as that which was released in the battle at Ypres was used to exterminate cockroaches, eliminate 7,000,000 people during the atrocities of the Holocaust and implement capital punishment in gas chambers across the United States of America.

The Slapstick Body
is existentially at odds with the world.

The Slapstick Body
has an irrational, disorderly relation to human life.

How do we consider an act or the product of an action to have value? How do we measure success? Must the one measuring and the one acting or producing be working to the same criteria? What if the one measuring and the one acting or producing are working to different criteria? What if an action or the product of an action suggests – demands even – a new criterion? And what if one simply does not care, remains totally indifferent to the measure? These questions are posed by art, war and death. In their answer lies the balance of power inherent to the act of judgement.

The Slapstick Body
is the surest way to undermine authority.

The Slapstick Body
is the last man standing before he falls.

In 1951, the United States Civil Defense Department released a short film introducing schoolchildren to the 'duck and cover' method of personal protection, intended to counter the lethal effects of a surprise nuclear attack. The method itself was presented in the film by Bert the Turtle. The film instructs, in the event of a sudden flash of bright light or similar indication of atomic attack, to take cover immediately under some kind of object, a desk or a table, and assume a prone position, covering neck and heads with the hands. Assuming this position, one resembles a turtle. This explains why the film is narrated by a turtle. Offering these instructions to the general public, the Civil Defense Department hoped to counter the natural human impulse to go and look for the source of disturbance. Testimony from the bombings of Hiroshima and Nagasaki confirmed that, upon seeing a flash of bright light more brilliant than the sun, more brilliant even than a thousand suns, as if the sky were suddenly lit by a whole universe of stars whose light we never see, never can see, because they are too far away for that light ever to reach us, the average person was inclined to move from whatever place they were in and venture towards a window in search of the source of this brilliance. Having done so, this person was immediately burned and blinded by the intense heat and light of the first blast and/or fell victim to the second, slower-moving blast whose waves, arriving at the window, created a pressure differential either side of the glass, deforming its surface to such an extent that it first became convex and, a split-second later, shattered into a thousand tiny pieces – projectiles flying at extreme velocity through the air. And it was the relationship of proximity between this average person and the window that guaranteed that these multiple fragments would pierce the layers of the outer self, epidermis, dermis and subcutaneous tissue, before digging deeper down and embedding into either flesh or bone. Such were the effects that the duck and cover method was conceived to counter. What is more, its effectiveness as a method of personal protection extended beyond such man-made catastrophes: the method has also been taught in areas prone to tornados, earthquakes and other natural disasters. All of this is comforting as we begin to imagine schoolchildren and adults all over the United States – all over the world, even, as this service message eventually began to spread more globally– curled up under desks and tables, hands covering their heads, waiting patiently like a turtle for the sky to fall.

The Slapstick Body
sits in chair in a film by Samuel Beckett.

Thwarted by machine, nature and other men, The Slapstick Body remains indifferent.

24 seconds

It is both real and not real, of fact and of fiction, that this man who plays the role of a man who is falling is really this man, Bas Jan Ader, who really is falling from a chair off a roof into bushes and losing one shoe.

22 seconds

Having decided to fall somewhere up ahead, the man sets off along the canal and rides for a very short while before arriving at a spot where he swerves his bicycle into the water and splash.

Belief stops thinking, so this scene is set for doubt as a man, tall, bipedal and wavering between his decision to stay upright or to lean his weight slightly more to the right lifts his left leg off the ground to test his balance, out of which he appears to be, although it could be the wind that blows him that way, the force of it bending the hedge either side of this path where his long, weedy frame mimics their supple bend but, of course, they are rooted, and he is not, and this makes his incline seem much more uncertain, his left foot touching the ground and lifting off, his left foot touching the ground and lifting off, his upper torso leaning further to the right and he, an imperfect triangle, eventually falling on another, the perfect triangle of a wooden trestle table; meanwhile, a building stands upright and unbending behind him.

1 minute 58 seconds

It is not fate but deliberation that brings this man to the branch of a tree whose roots are growing so close to the water, whose leaves are scant – it must be the winter – whose limbs are supporting the length of his body that dangles so oddly right over the water as he just hangs there ... he just hangs there ... as though in further deliberation or as if waiting for something to happen or like an ape that is out of proportion or maybe a piece of fruit that is ripening, that has ripened, and now dangles from the branch of this tree; it hangs there, and it will continue to hang there, until reaching that point when gravity's pull becomes too strong for its slight stem to stave and it falls off the branch and into the water and sinks below the surface and settles into the bottom where it will either seed or else it will rot in this shallow bed, in this mud.

3 minutes 26 seconds

We find ourselves with a man in a closed chamber filled by artificial light – that is, we find ourselves imaginatively projecting ourselves into a room with a man who stands between two sources of artificial light, between which sits a large rock, behind which stands the man, and all of which suggests a diurnal circuit inside of which we find ourselves with this man who appears to be waiting so patiently for his own action to begin: for his long legs to bend, for his body to fold, for his arms to extend and his hands to grasp firmly the rock that he turns, that he turns again (it's so heavy), that he lifts up into his arms and onto his shoulder where it rests, balanced by one of his hands, as he stands there like Atlas with a metonym of the world on his shoulder – and we sit here with him in this closed room with its artificial light and its part-world anticipating his next move, or perhaps just watching the length of his impossible body start to curve out of compensation for the weight of his fragment of world; or perhaps thinking why it is in the first place that this man is standing in this room with two sources of light and a piece of world that he struggles to hold up: what brought him here, his face gives nothing away – no story, no narrative – although we feel drawn to him, if only because it is clear that he is struggling, which makes us wonder why he decided to lift this fragment of the world in the first place, why he didn't just let it remain on the ground, why this need to struggle and then, after a time, we get a sense that something is about to happen: he might just drop it, he might just start crying and then what would we do, enclosed in a room with a man who is crying, but soon we forget this because it is clear that he is not going to cry and, instead, something else is about to happen: a change or a shift in this tragic composition as, suddenly, the man drops his piece of the world and lets it falls straight onto a source of the light, which goes out, but not the other light, which means that we find ourselves now in the half-light in this room with this man who had been struggling

F
A
L
L
I
N
G

but who, having decided let go of the world, is no longer struggling and this makes us think, however briefly, about human action, its consequence and, ultimately, whether the tragedies that befall us, that will befall us, are the result of purposely planned and rationally administrated choice.

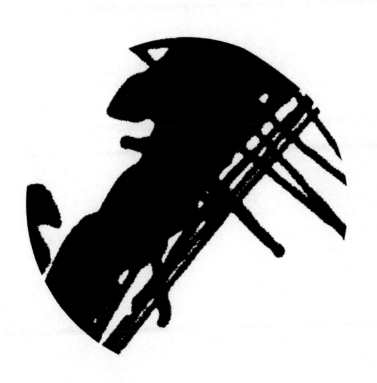

For a sign to become a sign, it must be repeated at least once. Which is why, when you witnessed the second crash into the second tower, you knew that this was not some random act of violence – the collision was no accident. This was an intentional act that, reiterated, carried meaning. Combat fought on a plane of representation: a sign of warfare's entry into the realm of the Symbolic where we portray and construct our lived reality through systems of learned association.

You commented how 'like a movie' it all seemed. Perhaps this was because you witnessed it through video footage playing in a continuous loop on a screen, although that particular mode of reception seems more suggestive of video art than 'the movies'. So perhaps it was because the scene itself seemed to mimic the familiar tropes of Hollywood film: 'Large US city under attack by aliens/terrorists/natural disaster. Cut to the Oval Office with scenes of controlled panic. Cut to suburbia with scenes of blissful oblivion disrupted by televised broadcast of large US city under attack by aliens/terrorists/natural disaster.' Susan Sontag observes how the phrase 'like a movie' seems to have eclipsed the invocation of 'like a dream' to characterise our contemporary experience of witnessing atrocity. Perhaps, then, it was the fact that, however fictitious or unreal the scene before you appeared, you knew that it was not a construct of the mind. You knew that those were real buildings and real planes and real bodies that were becoming signs in your political imaginary. Why could you not recognise this before?

As each plane collided into each tower it created an enormous explosion: a giant fireball erupting from the gash that cut across each tower. You see the orange blazing against the crisp azure sky, a perfect compositional counterbalance to the vertical precision of each steel and concrete structure.

Richard Drew explains how, as a photographer, he has become habituated to viewing the world through his camera: his reality framed, augmented by its appearance to him through his own manipulation of it as image. The camera acts like a shield, he says, allowing him to witness events that might otherwise be too overwhelming to bear. For example, he held a camera between himself and Robert Kennedy when taking that shot. Drew was working on a photo shoot for City Fashion Week when he was alerted to the situation in downtown Manhattan. He immediately got onto the subway and headed into town. No one was riding in the carriage with him. When he arrived at the scene there were people standing all around the streets watching the events unfold. You can hear them talking and gasping if you watch the footage on Youtube.

What you don't see is how the air inside each of the towers was beginning to thicken with a toxic cloud. The verticality of the structure meant that it was analogous to a chimney, sweeping the fumes emitted from each explosion up through the layers of the building and filling all of the floors above the crash site with an impossible smoke.

Sometimes you have a choice. Sometimes you have a decision thrust upon you, in which case you still must choose how to react. So there is no point pretending that your ethics don't bear any relation to your politics.

One second, split. One decisive act caught up as image and splintering into countless fragments of narrative, each composed uniquely in the mind of the viewer. Most often, that composition can be reconfigured easily into a recognisable whole. Something familiar that confirms the world you live in and your place in that world. Overcoming a Monster. Voyage and Return. Rebirth. However, in some instances, an image will resist this kind of reading. The image, or some aspect or detail of the image, will push against – or pull away – from the standard plot or storyline. Confronted with such an image your thoughts remain untethered. Your imagination drifts, simply floating away.

People often say that diving must be like flying. You hear this, for example, when the ten meter diving competition comes on during the Olympics and each supple body lifts off of the platform and into the air. 'It must be like flying,' they say. But they are wrong. Diving isn't at all like flying. It's like falling with control. It's like the definition of grace.

There were ten out-takes of the shot, approximately one for each second of the fall. Out of these shots, the image that was published, that was made public, is the one where the man is almost vertical, his body in near perfect alignment with the structure behind him. The almost satisfying quality of this composition is, of course, a product of pure chance. In each of the other shots the man is simply tumbling over and over again, his arms and legs flailing, his body beyond control.

That famous photograph by Yve Klein. His eyes are staring, his mouth is open, his arms are flung back behind him. Caught between the forces of gravity and wind, the wisps of his hair blow skyward. The artist would like to capture this moment, still timeless time as an act of will. But all of this is without consequence. Where we see as a slab of pavement he sees a tarpaulin cushioning his fall. History as a manipulation of image.

What is most uniquely identifiable about a person? Fingerprints? DNA? Voice? The retina of the eye? All of which completely exceeds what you know of this man. How, then, do you choose to know this falling man?

When people talk of any tragic event they often start with their own position in relation to it. 'I was in my kitchen … I was driving in my car … I was sitting at my desk … when I saw on TV … when I heard on the radio … when someone told me that.' The event becomes a story narrated from a first-person perspective. But what if the event is, in fact, a message directed to you, not something to which you are asked to bear witness? You spend weeks on the internet trying to figure out just what the message is saying and how you, in particular, are responsible.

You choose to know him as an individual. There he is, replete in his wholeness. One indivisible part of this great collectivity that is the starfish you. For him, this individual, you will grieve and you will fight. Meter out his worth in acts of vengeance. Of him you will tell countless stories to countless others, all of them beginning with your own person.

Due to public outcry, the photograph of the falling man was removed from circulation almost directly after its initial publication.

You choose to know him as face. Which is not to say that you actually see his face – you cannot. You know him as face through the crook of his leg. The way that his arms seem to be crossed, nonchalantly, behind his back. The way his shirt somehow doesn't seem right for the occasion and, besides, is still tucked in. You see him as face like that woman sitting across from you on the train the other day trying to be inconspicuous while eating a bar of chocolate, and who you loved.

A myth of origin: the man and the woman dwell in the Garden of Eden. They want for nothing. God says to them, 'You may freely eat of every tree of the garden; but of the tree of the knowledge of good and evil you shall not eat, for in the day that you eat of it you shall die.' The serpent then says to the woman, 'Did God say, "You shall not eat of any tree of the garden?"' And the woman replies, 'We may eat of the fruit of the trees of the garden; but God said, "You shall not eat of the fruit of the tree which is in the midst of the garden, neither shall you touch it, lest you die."' To which the serpent says 'You will not die. For God knows that when you eat of it your eyes will be opened, and you will be like God, knowing good and evil.' So the woman, seeking wisdom, eats of the tree and also gives some to the man. When God finds out that the man and the woman have eaten the fruit he says, 'Behold, the man has become like one of us, knowing good and evil; and now, lest he put forth his hand and take also of the tree of life, and eat, and live forever' – therefore God banishes the man and the woman from the garden forever. This is the story of original sin and a fall from grace into knowledge, an apparent correlation between human will and the natural laws of gravity.

You choose an unrecognisable death. One that does not fit with the heroic narrative and so becomes edited out of their stories. Removed from circulation. When asked how many of you there are the coroners deny that you even existed. There were no acts of will, they say, no gestures of refusal or passive resistance. There were only forces and those who were subject to them. So you become invisible, falling outside of history and out of their war.

Another origin: the child, seeking freedom and independence, stands upright. The stance is precarious and the child wavers and falls. This will happen again. This continues to happen until the child finds balance and, so doing, intends to move. The body's weight shifts forward and the child falls. This will happen again, and continue to happen, until the child learns to move one foot in front of the other, catching the weight of the body as it falls. The child falls. This will happen again until

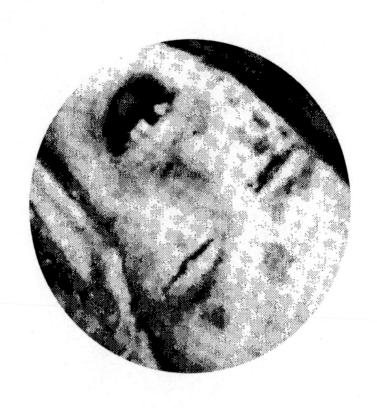

the child learns to embody the rhythm of one foot in front of the other, continually catching the weight of the body in its falling forward motion. The child walks, moving into measure.

There are others here with you, outside. Others who do not appear or who, when they do appear, remain unrecognisable. There is a man with black fabric covering his face who stands naked on a podium except for the wires. There is a woman with black fabric covering her face who is not a victim. There are people there on the ground behind that crosshair. There are others who are grieving, who we do not see. There are others who we see, but for whom we do not grieve. There are others who we see but do not see.

Is it into or out of thinking that you moved when you crossed that border into falling? When you stepped over the threshold between your worldly existence and a realm of pure force?

You are all falling and singing: a projection of self without measure.

Many witnesses spoke of how it sounded, as if that particular excess of spectacle made it all the more real. A heavy, dull thud. Like a bag of earth. Each distinct sounding in the constant, syncopated rhythm of bodies all straining toward matter.

The famous story by Franz Kafka. Its title suggests the movement across kingdoms, between species. 'Gregor woke one morning from uneasy dreams to find himself transformed into some kind of giant insect.' This first sentence seems startling for its abrupt transition, or transformation, from human into non-human; Gregor into insect. In fact, what makes it so startling is that there is no transition at all. There is simply Gregor, out of the world and insect in that first sentence. The transformation has already happened, the writing proceeds from there. In this sense, the story does not offer the cause, but only the effects of Gregor's metamorphosis; the repercussions of his tumble down the great chain of being.

You prefer this. Belly so close to the earth. The earth a vast, continual present – no horizon. Legs moving so many moving so many moving so fast so fast. You look all around and you are all eyes, all of you, you are all of you all eyes and no face. You are all of you on your bellies and in the dirt and in the mud and in the dust and of the world.

All of the turtles all over the world all waiting for the sky to fall.

Man at the extreme limits of contemporary warfare. His body sleek and eyeless. His voice a deep, continuous hum. He crosses borders, but has no fear when crossing borders, so does he really cross these borders? He does not die, he kills by proxy: through coordinate and image. Man as insect at the extreme limits of contemporary warfare.

Man, there is no man, there is not a man, there are no men, no men.

The measure of 'now' in one elongated footstep. You are falling. Your house is falling. Beneath your house, a bloodbath. Beneath the bloodbath, utopia. Beneath this, torture, death and terror in unknown quantity. A statue with blind eyeballs. Ideology as a map. A controlled collapse of structure and a sleek new symbol. Of impossible dimension. Your hyperbolic tendencies. Television, prosthetics and the visceral confusion of language. You feel love. The United States does not pick fights and, above all else, the complex iconicity of Ronald Reagan's face. Those men over there are taking pictures. You like the movies too. Sometimes you fight and other times you are instructed to remember. Perhaps all of this is absurd. The image as emblem and shrapnel. If it is no longer ethical to speak of disorientation, then imagine a leap into gravity. Contemplation and response. The frame administers itself. Have you ever tried thinking the contemporary state of global warfare *without* genre? Keep shoot'n. Keep shoot'n. Keep shoot'n. The body relies on others. As responsibility, so time converges on this 'now'

in a world under the world.
Animals. Insects. Dust. Now

                    everything flowers.

PAUL DE MAN
(1919–1983)
Belgian-born literary critic and theorist who considered untenable and unreliable any access to history through literature or narrative.

JOHN DEWEY
(1859–1952)
American Pragmatist philosopher, psychologist, educational reformer and inventor of the 'Dewey Decimal System' of library organisation.

IMMANUEL KANT
(1724–1804)
German philosopher who explored the relation between reason and human experience and never travelled more than 10 kilometres beyond his birthplace.

HEINRICH VON KLEIST
(1777–1811)
German novelist, dramatist, short-story writer and poet who believed that consciousness expresses a fall out of nature's harmony.

CATHERINE CLÉMENT
(1939–present)
French philosopher, novelist, feminist and literary critic who moves deftly and poetically through Eastern and Western philosophical traditions.

MAHATMA GANDHI
(1869–1948)
'The follower of truth and non-violence will offer *satyagraha* against tyranny and win over the tyrant by love.'

MICHEL SERRES
(1930–present)
A French philosopher of science known for his writing that is materially and figuratively rich; his ideas are bold and prophetic.

FILIPPO BRUNELLESCHI
(1377–1446)
Italian architect and engineer of the Renaissance most famous for his development of single-point perspective: a magician among conjurers.

HILDEGARD VON BINGEN
(1098–1179)
German writer, composer, philosopher, abbess, polymath and saint; most well known of the medieval Christian mystics and visionaries.

ST THOMAS OF AQUINAS
(1225–1274)
Italian Dominican friar and priest who discussed the nature, activities and moral state of angels whom he considered to be pure spirit.

ARISTOTLE
(384 BCE–322 BCE)
Ancient Greek philosopher for whom philosophy is 'the science of the universal essence of that which is actual'; it starts from particularity.

JOHN LOCKE
(1632–1704)
English philosopher and political theorist who founded the school of thought known as British Empiricism.

RENÉ DESCARTES
(1596–1650)
French philosopher whose strategy of hyperbolic doubt eventually led to a dualistic distinction between the immaterial mind and the body.

ELISHA OTIS
(1811–1861)
American self-taught mechanic whose inventions include the safety elevator, steam plough, rotary oven, and oscillating steam engine.

REM KOOLHAAS
(1944–present)
Dutch architect, architectural theorist and urbanist who celebrates the 'chance-like' nature of New York City.

MICHEL DE CERTEAU
(1925–1986)
French Jesuit scholar known for his theory of spatial practice; he also wrote on mysticism, phenomenology, psychoanalysis and religion.

TITUS LUCRETIUS CARUS
(99 BCE–55 BCE)
Ancient Roman poet and philosopher best known for his philosophical poem *De rerum natura* in which he defends atomist philosophy.

ÉMILE BENVENISTE
(1902–1976)
French structural theorist and semiotician known for his expansion of the linguistic theory through emphasis on discourse and the referent.

LEUCIPPUS

(480 BCE–420 BCE)

Ancient Greek philosopher and a founder of atomist doctrine who understood that worlds or kosmoi were formed from a cosmic whirl.

DEMOCRITUS

(460 BCE–370 BCE)

Ancient Greek philosopher known for his atomist doctrine; also known as the 'laughing philosopher' for his emphasis on value of cheerfulness.

PLATO

(427 BCE–347 BCE)

Ancient Greek philosopher who defined philosophy as the 'science of the ideal'; he saw universal essence as distinct from particular things.

FRANK BUNKER GILBRETH

(1868–1924)

American film-maker and advocate of scientific management who developed motion studies as a method of improving work efficiency.

FREDERICK WINSLOW TAYLOR

(1856–1915)

American mechanical engineer and inventor of scientific management to improve economic efficiency through labour productivity.

PETER SLOTERDIJK

(1947–present)

A German 'posthumanist' philosopher who often considers the inter-relationship between humans, animals, plants and machines.

SAMUEL BECKETT
(1906–1989)
Irish novelist, playwright, theatre director and poet; his only screenplay, *Film*, is based on the principle that 'to be is to be perceived'.

BAS JAN ADER
(1942–1975)
Dutch conceptual artist who used gravity as a medium and who set sail on a small boat across the Atlantic, never to be seen or heard from again.

SUSAN SONTAG
(1993–2004)
American essayist, activist and teacher noted for her clarity of thought and intellectual investment in art and politics.

RICHARD DREW
(1946–present)
American photojournalist best known for his image of *The Falling Man*; he was also present at the assassination of Robert F. Kennedy.

YVE KLEIN
(1928–1962)
French artist and inventor of IKB (International Klein Blue); also known for his photograph *Saut dans le vide* (Leap into the Void) (1960).

FRANZ KAFKA
(1883–1924)
'How wonderful that is, isn't it? The lilac – dying, it drinks, goes on swilling.'

§

VIT HOPLEY
Wednesday Afternoon

Wednesday Afternoon is a collection of prose that introduces awkward perspectives on all manner of things: a house taken on an arduous journey across a frozen lake, a puff of dust released from yesterday's socks, a death in a basement, a gathering of strangers. Vit Hopley pays attention to every detail. She writes on sitting, standing and lying down, but most significantly she creates a stillness that is almost photographic.

'Wednesday Afternoon *has shown words anew. It's very much like fresh rain and fresh air.'*

PHILIPPA BREWSTER

MICHAEL SCHWAB
Paris

Michael Schwab is curious about trees in Paris. The most unnatural thing about a tree in a city is the place where it is planted. A tree in a city does not grow; it is planted. *Paris* lets you explore trees in Paris while it breaches narrow definitions of photography.

'*So you think you know Paris, but if you take Michael Schwab as your guide you will find yourself in a truly inventive space between photography and drawing. You will be delightfully transported to spaces and places of the imagination, with some very particular trees to hold on to for reality. This is indeed Paris from another perspective.'*

VANESSA JACKSON

JASPAR JOSEPH-LESTER
Revisiting the Bonaventure Hotel

This book is a photo-essay that describes the life of a building through a range of film stills, photographic images and written citations. With *Revisiting the Bonaventure Hotel* we wander between references to Fredric Jameson, John Portman and Arnold Schwarzenegger as we view a world through different perspectives: vertical, horizontal and rotating. This is a story about the image.

'I loved it. Looks like a Chris Marker book, so glamorous.'
CHRIS KRAUS

HAYLEY NEWMAN
Common

Through fact and fiction, questions and answers, writings from the heart and writing from the street, *Common* chronicles one day of a Self-Appointed Artist-in-Residence in the City of London. Performances occur and reoccur as this book takes us to crashes in global markets, turbulence in the Euro-zone, riots on hot summer nights and the most extraordinary imaginings.

'The financial sector in the City of London is often viewed as an impermeable, inaccessible block, and that perception is what gives it a lot of its power. In Common, *Hayley Newman has subverted that, opening the City up through richly imaginative stories that are at once creative examples of how to play with the space, and empowering political actions. I hope this book will inspire others to embark on similar transformative adventures.'*
BRETT SCOTT

ANNE TALLENTIRE
Object of a Life

Oscillating between depiction and description, *Object of a Life* addresses the question: How are we to speak of common things? Making an inventory of things that come to hand in the course of daily life, playing with ideas of contradiction, categorisation, improbability and speculation, this book offers an articulation of the space produced between language and drawing.

'In Object of a Life *Anne Tallentire extends her enquiry past the objects of everyday life to ruminate on the space in between and around the objects' relationship to their sites of activity including the domestic, the studio and the street. Like all good artists' writing, this book calls upon us to think differently...'*
LISA PANTING

JAKI IRVINE
Days of Surrender

In 1916, when Padraic Pearse, Irish republican and leader of the 'Easter Rising', decided to surrender, he asked midwife Elizabeth O'Farrell to make the perilous walk to deliver his message to the British army. Setting off down a Dublin street where some of the dead still held white flags in their hands, Elizabeth O'Farrell was watched from the door by Julia Grenan, referred to in documents as her 'friend and lifelong companion.' This is the story of those days.

DIAGRAMS FOR SERIALITY
Neil Chapman

Diagrams for Seriality is a book of unforgettable images and strange characters. Here the reader is thrown into a world where expectations of series and sequence are turned inside out; this story creates a narrative of haunting and mysterious affect.

'A startling meditation on the relation of seeing to saying, the possibility and impossibility of communication, and the very business of making and writing – Diagrams for Seriality is a work of fictioning in which set pieces and scenes, a cast of bodies and conceptual personae and a singular prose style produce a book that demands to be reread.'

SIMON O'SULLIVAN

Common Intellectual series

Current Editions

Future Editions

For future editions, please visit the Copy Press website

Copy Press is committed to bringing readers and writers together and invites you to join its Reader's Union – please visit www.copypress.co.uk